THE SCRIBNER
RADIO MUSIC LIBRARY

Edited by
ALBERT E. WIER

VOLUME V
LIGHT OPERA AND BALLET
EXCERPTS
. . .
PIANO

NEW YORK
CHARLES SCRIBNER'S SONS

THE SCRIBNER RADIO MUSIC LIBRARY

VOLUME V—EXCERPTS FROM BALLETS AND LIGHT OPERAS

TABLE OF CONTENTS—TITLES

THE SCRIBNER RADIO MUSIC LIBRARY

VOLUME V—EXCERPTS FROM BALLETS AND LIGHT OPERAS

TABLE OF CONTENTS—COMPOSERS

A Guide Through Volume V

THE volumes of the SCRIBNER RADIO MUSIC LIBRARY are devoted entirely to compositions which are heard constantly over the great broadcasting chains—played by orchestras, chamber music organizations or instrumental soloists; sung by choral organizations or by vocal soloists. Each of the nine volumes contains only the choicest and most popular of its particular type of music.

This volume is devoted to excerpts from light operas, ballets, and orchestral suites universally popular with the radio audience. Many of the light operas have been presented in practically complete form over the larger broadcasting chains, while every day we hear individual songs and instrumental selections from them.

FRENCH LIGHT OPERAS

French light-opera composers contribute liberally to the contents of this volume—there is the overture to Adolphe Adams' tuneful operetta, **If I Were King**, a tale of the vagabond poet, François Villon; Edmond Audran's two lively operettas, **The Mascot** and **Olivette**, contain many melodies familiar to the radio music lover. One of the most important French grand-opera composers, Daniel Auber, conceived an operetta entitled **Fra Diavolo**, of which the overture and several songs, especially "On Yonder Rock Reclining," are extremely popular. We often hear on the air strains from Lecocq's **Giroflé-Girofla**, an amusing and melodious operetta in which the famous comic-opera star, Lillian Russell, charmed her audiences for many years. In the opinion of many, Jacques Offenbach was the greatest of French light-opera composers, as he was also one of the most prolific. Excerpts from **The Grand Duchess**, also a starring vehicle for Lillian Russell, the overture to **Orpheus in the Underworld**, and the "Barcarolle" from **The Tales of Hoffman** are constantly played and sung. The French list concludes with Robert Planquette's charming romantic operetta, **The Chimes of Normandy**, which has been heard many times in complete form.

GERMAN AND VIENNESE LIGHT OPERAS

Franz von Suppé, the indefatigible composer of more than four hundred light operas, or "Singspieler" as they were called in his native land, contributes mightily to the enjoyment of radio music lovers through the overture to **Poet and Peasant**, and the equally pleasing overture to **Light Cavalry**, while selections, both vocal and instrumental, from **Fatinitza** are often broadcast. Another favorite is the overture to Otto Nicolai's musical version of **The Merry Wives of Windsor**; Karl Millocker's **Beggar Student** has been broadcast in complete form many times, and we often hear the touching "Es Hat Nicht Sollen Sein" from Victor Nessler's **Trumpeter of Sakkingen**. In modern days, Viennese composers have achieved international reputation with their light operas; in this volume we have selections from Franz Lehar's **Merry Widow** and from the bewitching **Waltz Dream** by Oscar Straus.

GILBERT AND SULLIVAN OPERAS

In the English light and comic opera field, two names stand out above all others—Gilbert and Sullivan—collaborators in more than twelve amusing and tuneful creations in which the perfection of the lyrics is equalled only by the exquisite art of the composer in conceiving melodies exactly suited to them. Nearly all of these twelve operas have been presented in complete form over the radio, and selections from nine of them are to be found in this volume. First there is **The Gondoliers**, a finely wrought satire on the Italian grand opera; then comes **H. M. S. Pinafore**, a musical caricature of antiquated methods in the British navy; then **The Mikado**, which greatly worried the British authorities through the possibility of its giving offense to the Japanese.   Another operetta poked sly fun at the British peerage—**Iolanthe** —and still another one pointed the finger of satire at Oscar Wilde and those of his cult in **Patience**.   The slow, pompous, and irrational methods of British court procedure were satirized in **Trial by Jury,** and the ridiculous aspects of superstition in **Ruddygore.**   Only one of the Gilbert and Sullivan operas was really purely romantic in character—**The Yeomen of the Guard**—this being perhaps the reason that it was least successful because their public had grown to expect only satire.   The selections in this volume contain the melodies which are most popular in each opera, and many enjoyable hours may be spent with them.   Another English opera, which has also been radioed complete, is Edward Jakobowski's **Erminie,** containing the exquisite "Lullaby."

FAMOUS BALLET MUSIC   In the field of ballet music, the French composer, Lèo Delibes, leads in popularity.   There is the exquisite **Naïla** from which every one loves the "Valse des Fleurs"; then there is **Sylvia** with the lively "Pizzicato," the tender "Barcarolle," and the alluring "Valse Lente."   Still another very popular Delibes ballet, from which we often hear selections, is **Coppelia** with its cleverly mechanical "Doll Waltz," its fiery "Czardas," its stirring "Mazurka," and its lovely "Valse Lente."   Charles Gounod has conceived exquisitely appropriate ballet music for the grand opera **Faust,** which we never seem to tire of hearing over the air.   The Russian composers, probably on account of the lavish splendor with which the Czars were accustomed to mount ballets in the Imperial Opera Houses, were particularly drawn to this field of composition, and there are excerpts in this volume from Tschaikowsky's ballet of fairyland entitled **The Nutcracker,** and another ballet, drawn from fairy-tale sources, called **The Sleeping Beauty.**   Still another Russian has contributed a splendid work of its kind to ballet-music literature—Alexander Glazounow with his **Raymonda,** given originally in scenes of sumptuous splendor at the Russian Imperial Opera in Petrograd.

ORCHESTRAL SUITES   Several orchestral suites meet with great favor from the radio audience when they are broadcast, and foremost among these is the Russian composer, Ippolitow-Iwanow's **Caucasian Sketches,** which the author claims is founded on melodies heard in the Caucasian villages and mountain passes.   The last movement, "Entrance of the Sardar," the opening phrase of which reminds one of Stephen Foster's "Old Black Joe," is perhaps the most popular and it is given complete in this volume.   Another very popular suite in Spanish style is Paul Lacome's **La Feria** which, while written by a Frenchman, is quite as Spanish in its musical atmosphere as if written by a native.   Under the attractive, although not musically significant, title **Egyptian Ballet,** Alexander Luigini has conceived a suite of fanciful compositions which have become entirely familiar to the radio audience.

The Nut-Cracker
(Casse-Noisette)
Ballet

P. Tschaikowsky

Allegro guisto (Miniature Overture)

Commodo (Arabian Dance)

Molto vivace (Trepak)

(Valse des Fleurs)

The Sleeping Beauty

Ballet

Tempo di Valse

P. Tschaikowsky

To Coda ⊕

Faust
Ballet Music

Charles Gounod

Allegretto, mouvement de Valse

(Ballet movement Nº1)

Adagio

(Ballet movement No. 2)

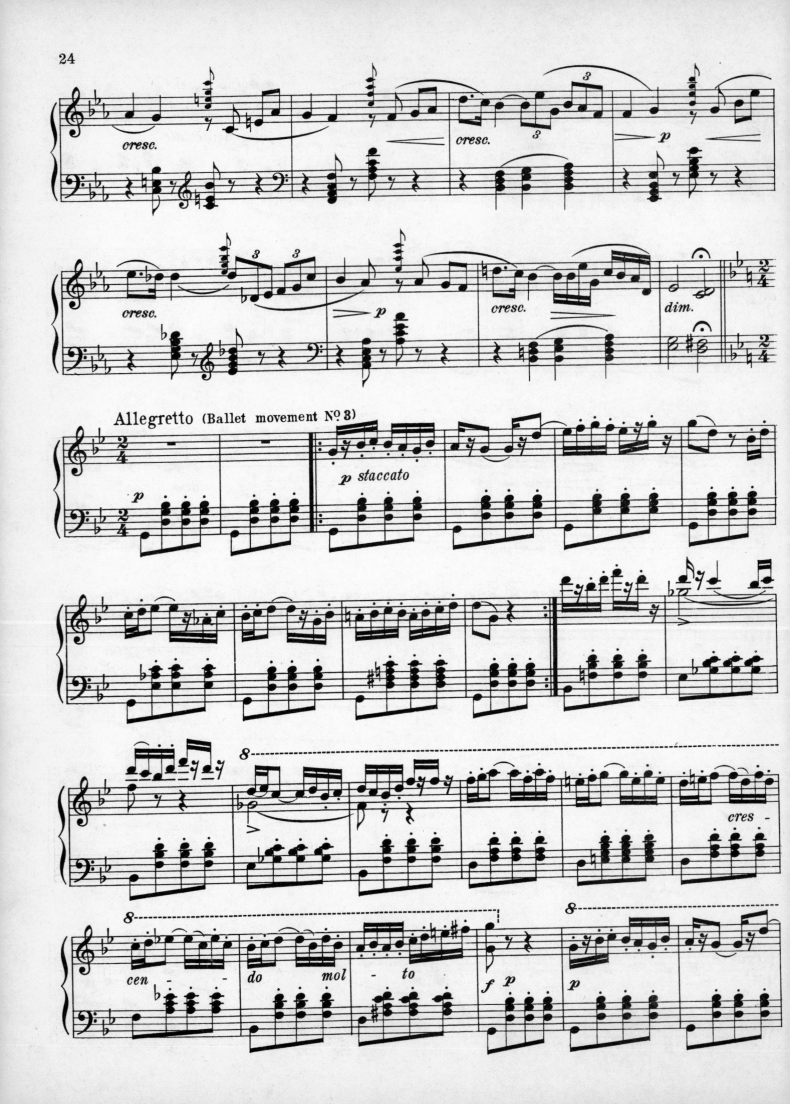

Allegretto (Ballet movement № 3)

Moderato maestoso (Ballet movement № 4)

Moderato con Moto (Ballet movement №5)

Allegretto (Ballet movement № 6)

Caucasian Sketches
(Procession of the Sardar)

M. Ippolitoff-Ivanoff

a tempo, poco più mosso

La Feria
Spanish Suite

P. LACOME

Allegro (Los Toros)

Allegretto (The Serenade)

Tempo di Valse (Zarzuela)

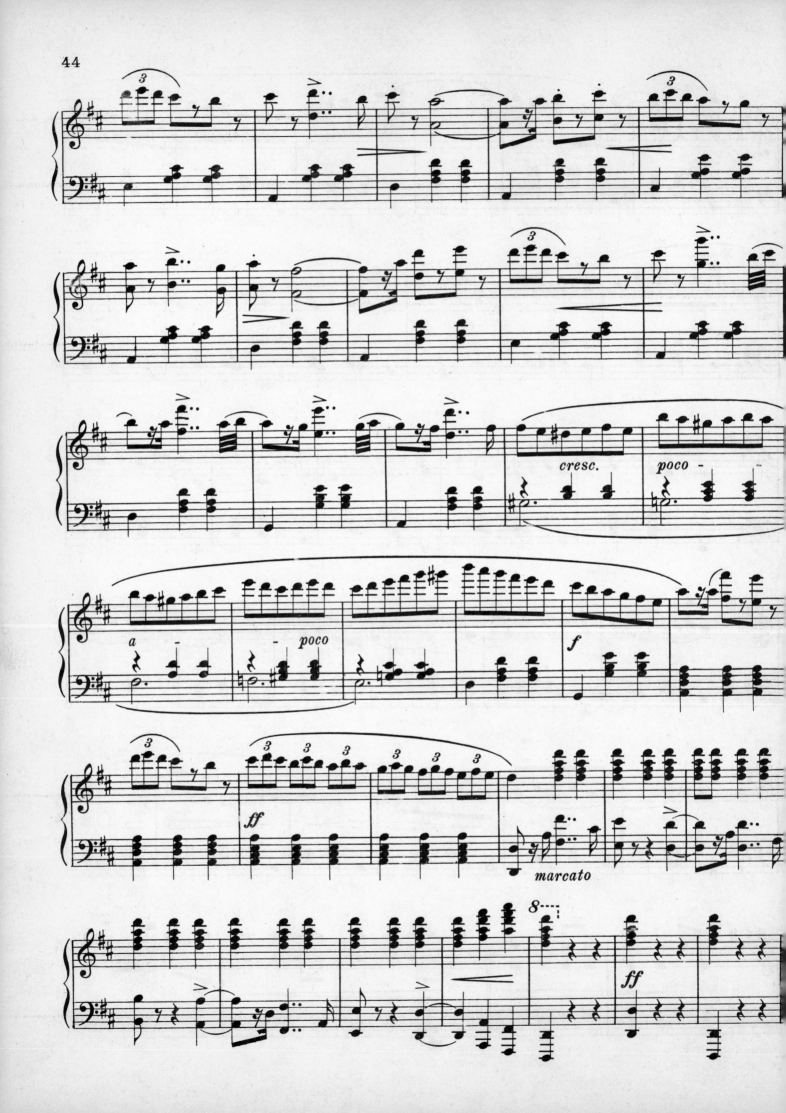

Egyptian Ballet
(Excerpts)

A. Luigini

Allegro non troppo

Allegretto

aussi piano que possible

Allegro non troppo

Coppelia

Valse Lente

Léo Delibes

Coppelia

Mazurka and Czardas

Leo Delibes

Allegro marcato (Mazurka)

Allegro marcato

Moderato (Czardas)

Largement et très marqué

Allegretto

Plus animé

Coppelia

Valse de la Poupée
(Doll Waltz)

Léo Delibes

Allegro moderato

Tempo di Valse

Naïla

(Pas des Fleurs)

Léo Delibes

Sylvia
(Barcarolle et Valse lente)

Lèo Delibes

Andante sans lenteur (Barcarolle)

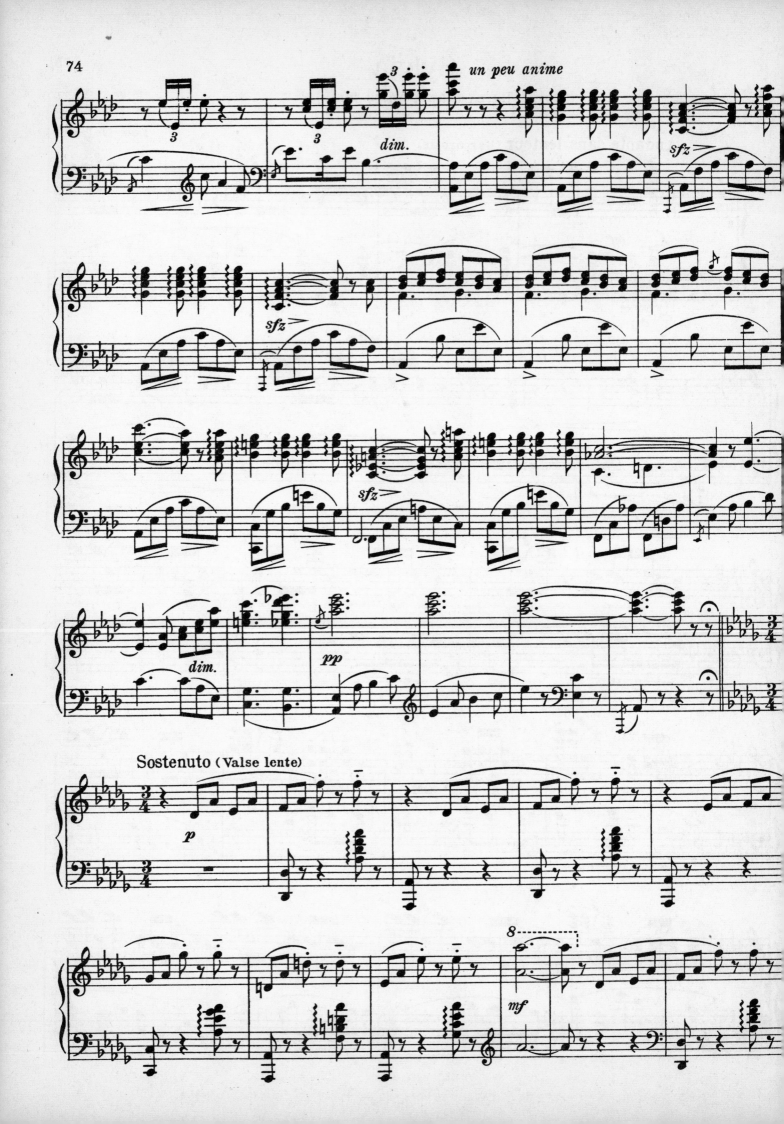

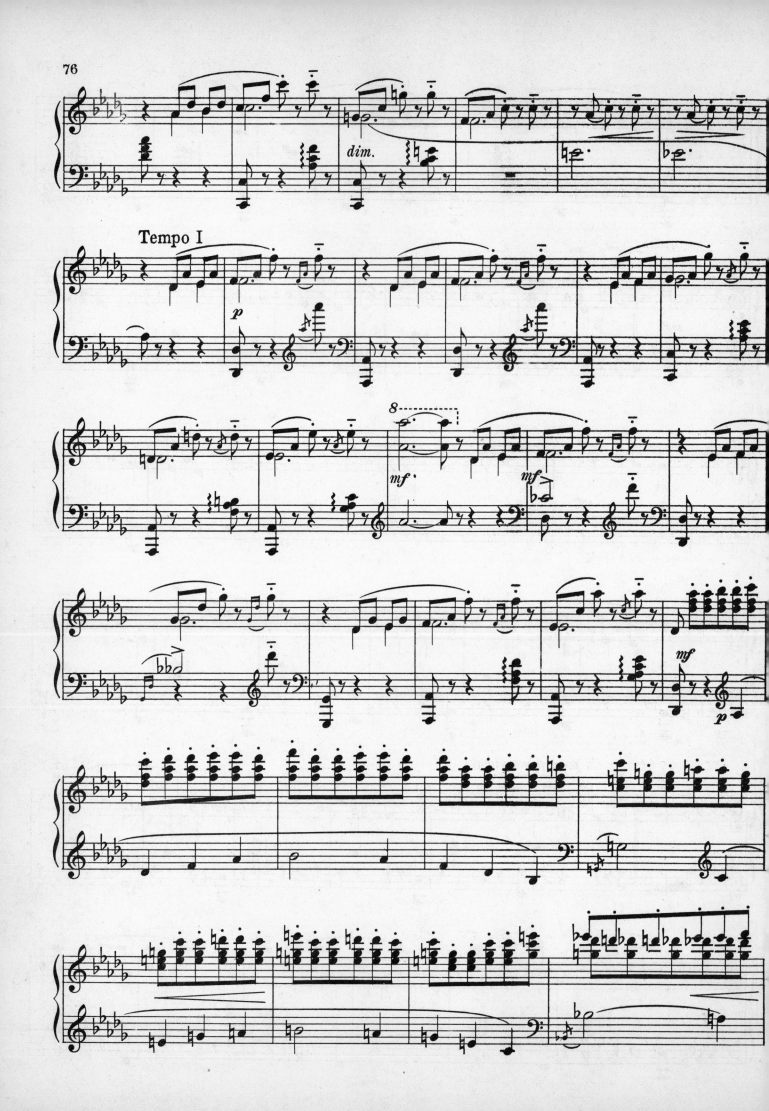

Sylvia
(Pizzicati)

Léo Delibes

Allegretto ben moderato

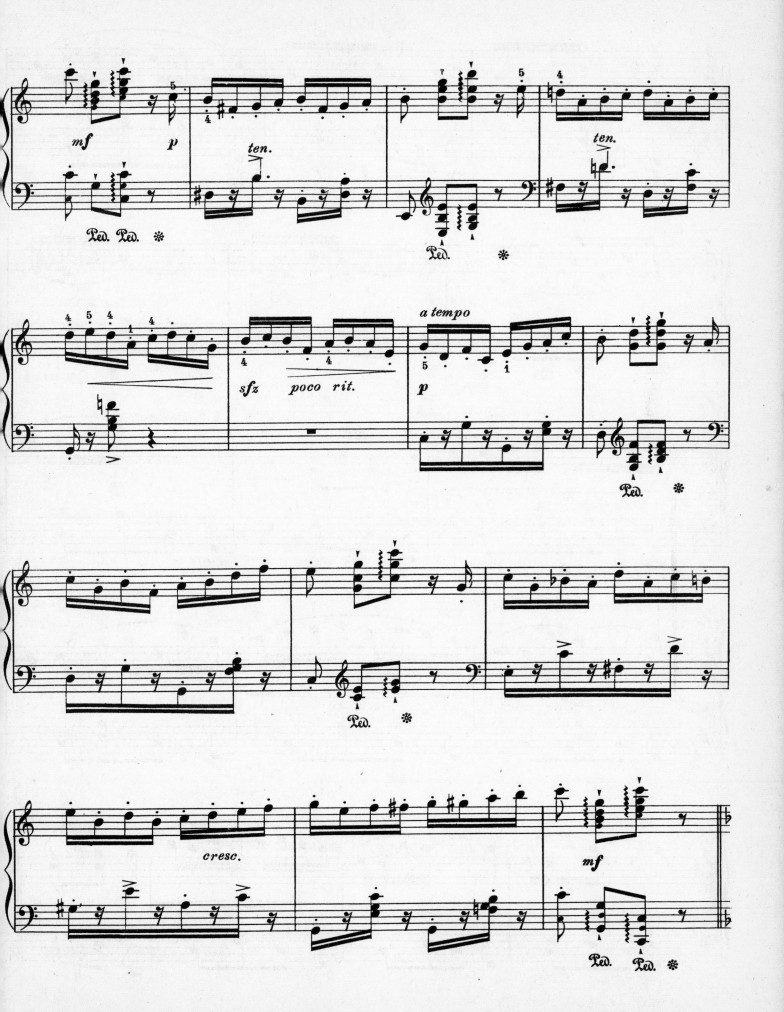

Raymonda
Ballet

A. Glazounow

Moderato molto (La Romanesca)

Tempo di Valse Lente (Valse Fantastique)

Più animato

The Merry Wives of Windsor

(Excerpts from the Overture)

Otto Nicolai

Andantino moderato

Fra Diavolo

Selected Melodies

D.F. Auber

Allegretto (On Yonder Rock Reclining)

Piú lento.

Allegretto (Chorus.)

Allegro (Overture)

The Mascot

Selected Melodies

E. Audran

Allegro (Opening Chorus)

Tempo di Valse (The Legend of the Mascot)

Andantino (Gobble Duet)

Tempo di Valse lento (A Loving Kiss)

Allegro vivo (Coaching Chorus)

sempre staccato

_ff_

_fz_   _fz_   _fz_   _simile_

Olivette
Selected Melodies

E. Audran

Vivace (The Torpedo and The Whale)

Waltz tempo (First Love)

Allegro (Bob Up Serenely)

Tempo di Valse (Ha! Ha! Ha!)

Allegro (The Farandole)

If I Were King
Selected Melodies

Adolphe Adam

a tempo

dim. e rit.

Andante (Cavatina)

f p

Ped. ※ Ped. ※ Ped. ※ Ped. ※ Ped. ※ Ped. ※ Ped. ※

simile

Allegretto (Finale to Overture)

Giroflé-Girofla

Selected Melodies

Ch. Lecocq

Allegretto (My Father's A Great Banker)

Tempo di Valse (Drinking Song)

Allegro (Matamoras, the valiant Captain)

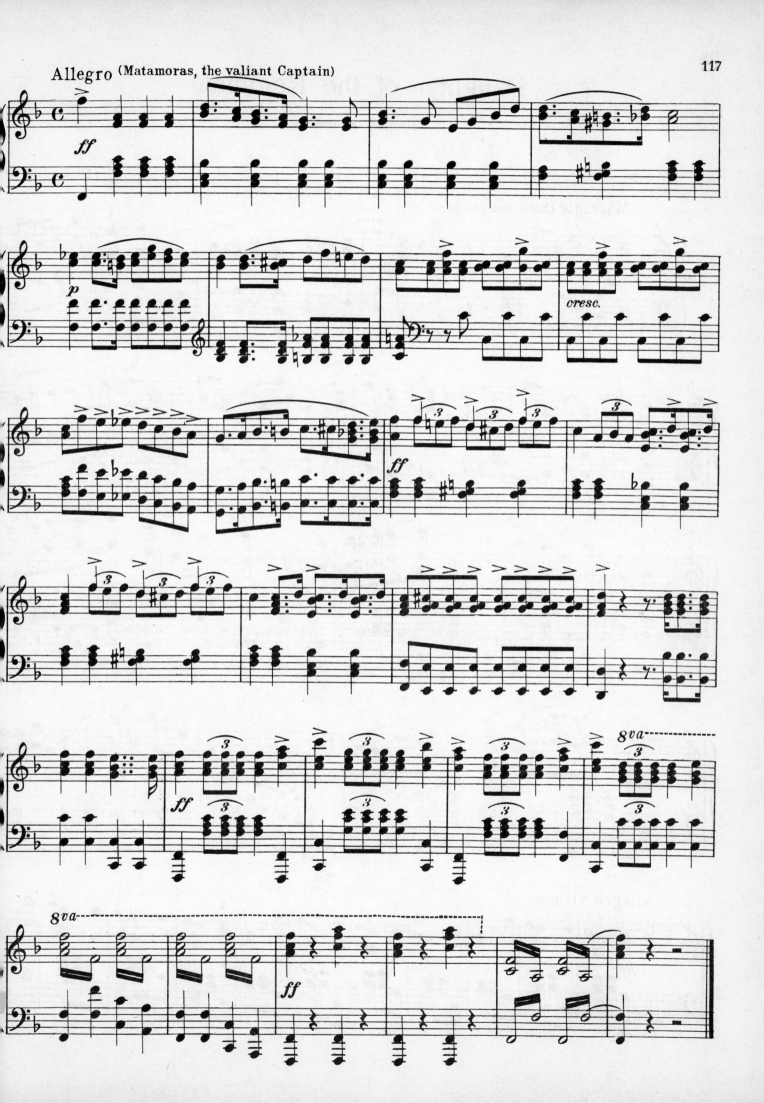

Daughter of the Regiment

Selected Melodies

G. Donizetti

Poet And Peasant

(Excerpts from the Overture)

Franz von Suppe

Andante maestoso

Allegretto

Fatinitza
Selected Melodies

Franz von Suppe

Allegretto

Allegro marziale (March Forward Fearlessly)

Light Cavalry
(Excerpts from the Overture)

Franz von Suppè

Andantino con moto (Czardas)

Tempo I (Overture)

simile

The Beggar Student

Selected Melodies

Carl Millocker

Moderato

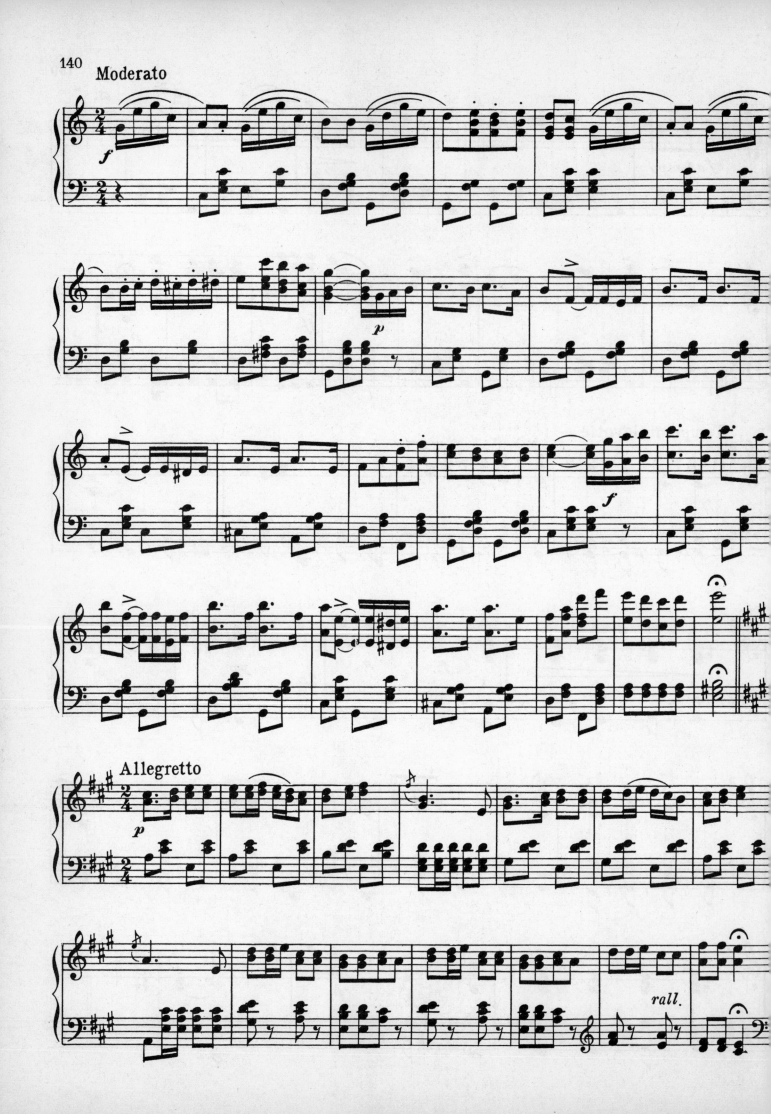

Vivo

Tempo di Marcia

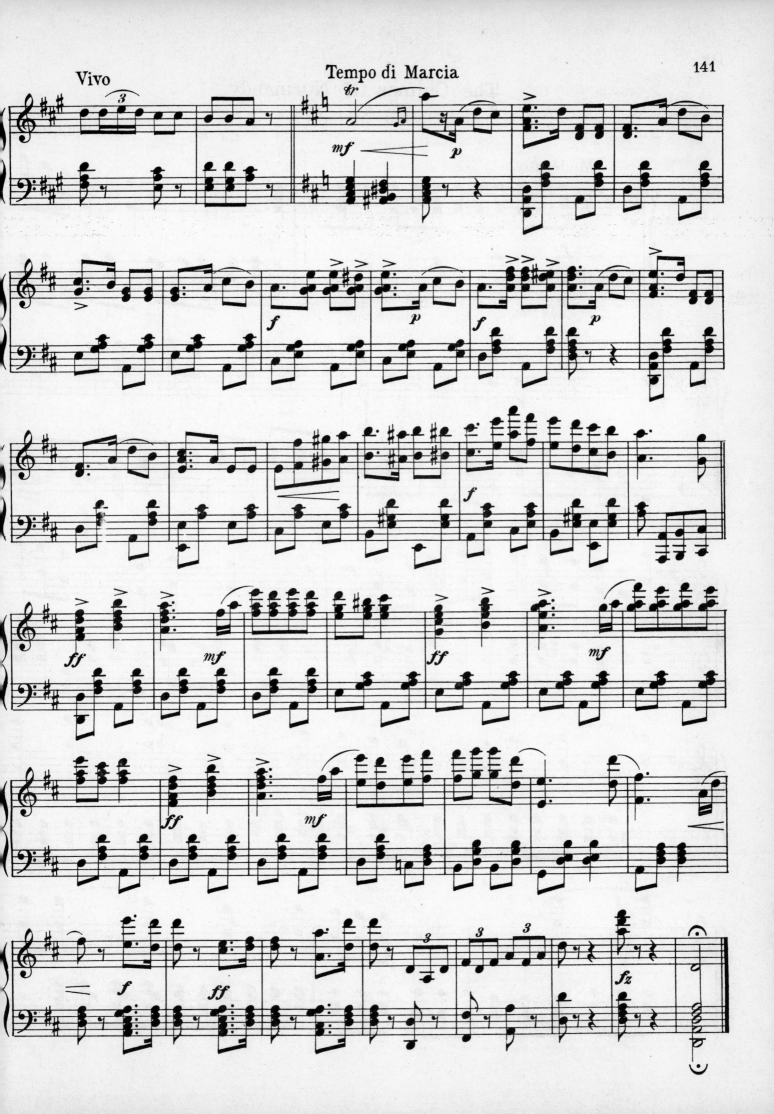

The Chimes Of Normandy
Selected Melodies

R. Planquette

Tempo di Valse (Waltz Song)

Allegro

Moderato (Barcarolle)

Tempo di Valse (Waltz)

The Trumpeter of Sakkingen

Selected Melodies

Victor Nessler

Erminie
Selected Melodies

E. Jakobowski

Tempo di Valse (Dream Song)

Tempo di Gavotte (Graceful Dance)

Allegretto (When Love Is Young)

March Tempo (March)

Die Fledermaus (The Bat)

Selected Melodies

Johann Strauss

Tempo di Valse (Waltz)

(Ah, what a Feast, what a Night of Joy)

The Queen's Lace Handkerchief

Selected Melodies

Johann Strauss

Tempo di Marcia (Now The King We Hail)

Moderato (Where the wild rose)

Allegretto (Ah! Nonsense 'Tis)

Tempo di Valse (Finale)

The Gipsy Baron

Selected Melodies

Johann Strauss

Tempo di Valse (Oh So Full Of Cheer)

Molto Vivace (I See a Day)

Tempo di Valse (It's a charming Profession)

Vivace (With my Porkers)

Orpheus In The Underworld
(Excerpts from the Overture)

J. Offenbach

Allegro con fuoco

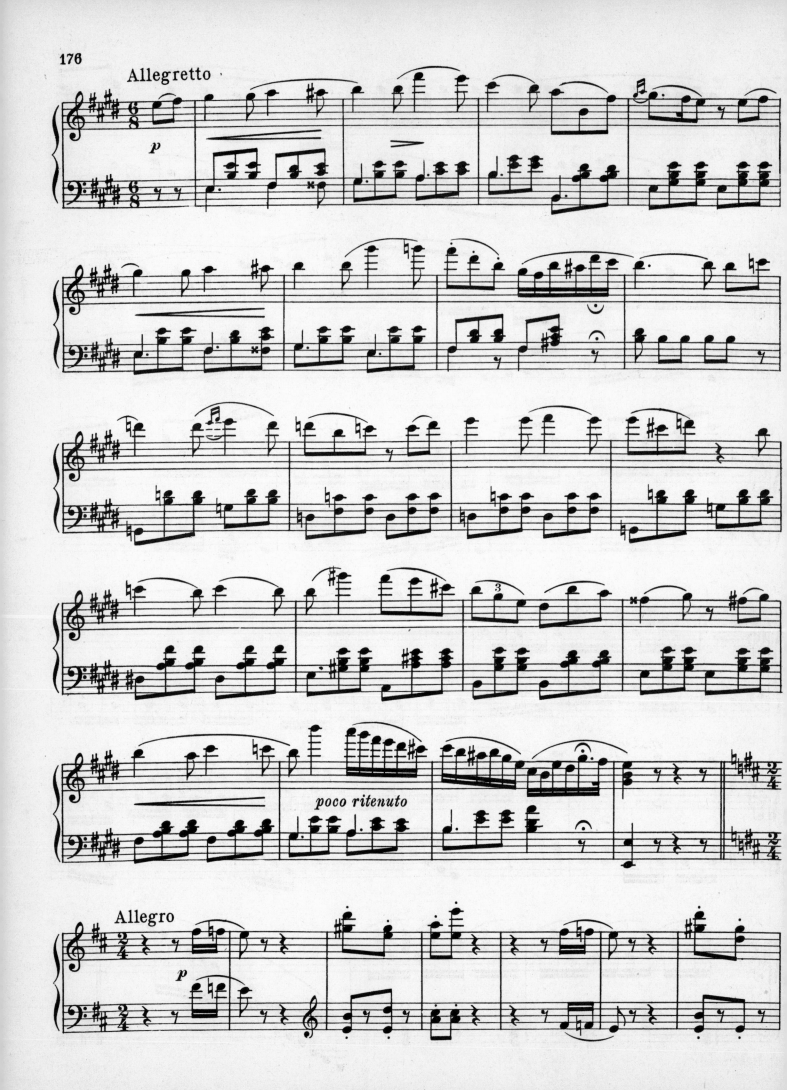

Allegro moderato (Galop)

p et staccato

The Grand Duchess
Selected Melodies

J. Offenbach

Andante (Behold My Father's Sword)

Allegro vivace (I Love The Military)

Tempo di Marcia (A Famous Regiment)

The Tales of Hoffmann
Barcarolle

J. Offenbach

A Waltz Dream
Selected Melodies

O. Straus

Allegretto moderato (A Maiden So Lovely)

Andantino quasi allegretto (Entr'acte)

Allegretto (Love Duet)

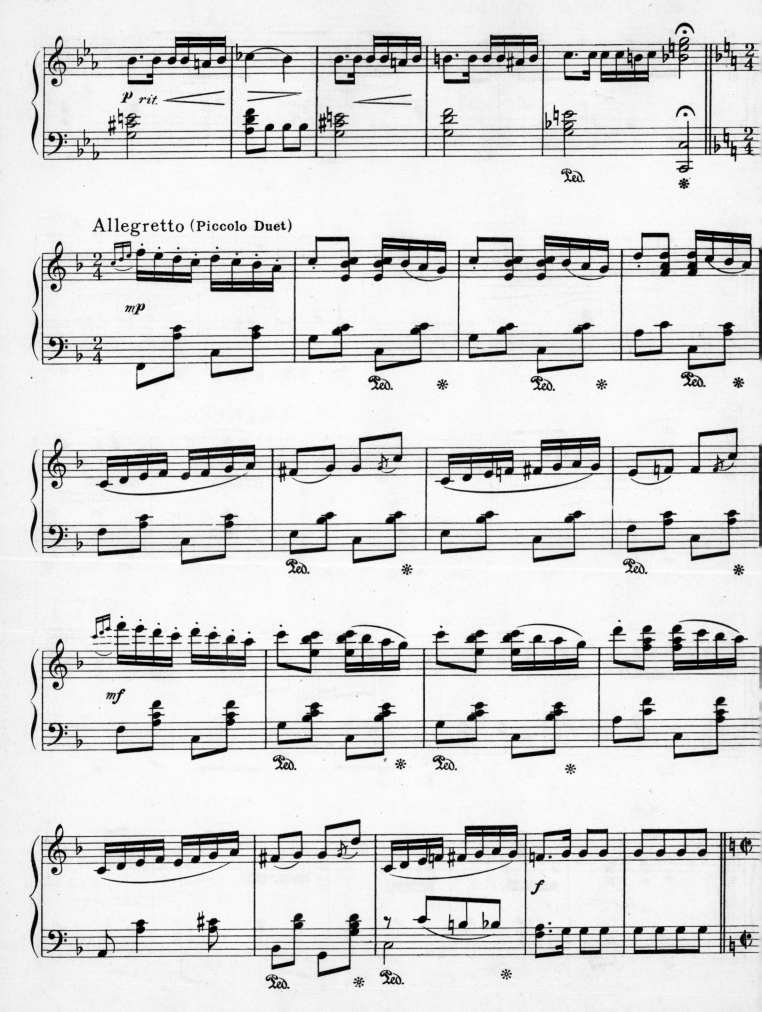

Allegretto (Piccolo Duet)

Tempo di Marcia (Whistling Song)

The Merry Widow

Selected Melodies

Franz Lehar

Tempo di Valse lente

Tempo di Valse From Finale-Act I

Andantino (Vilia Song)

Allegro (The Study of Woman)

Trial By Jury

Selected Melodies

Arthur Sullivan

Allegro vivace (Opening Chorus)

Allegretto (Defendant's Song)

Allegro grazioso (Bridesmaid's Chorus)

Vivace (Defendant and Plaintiff's Duet)

The Yeomen of the Guard
Selected Melodies

Arthur Sullivan

Allegro Marziale (The Tower Song)

Allegretto (When A Maiden Loves)

Tempo di Gavotte (Quartet "Strange Adventure")

Andante espressivo (Is Life A Boon?)

Allegro con brio (The Merryman and his Maid)

The Pirates Of Penzance
Selected Melodies

Arthur Sullivan

Allegro maestoso

(When Frederic Was A Little Lad)
Allegro pesante

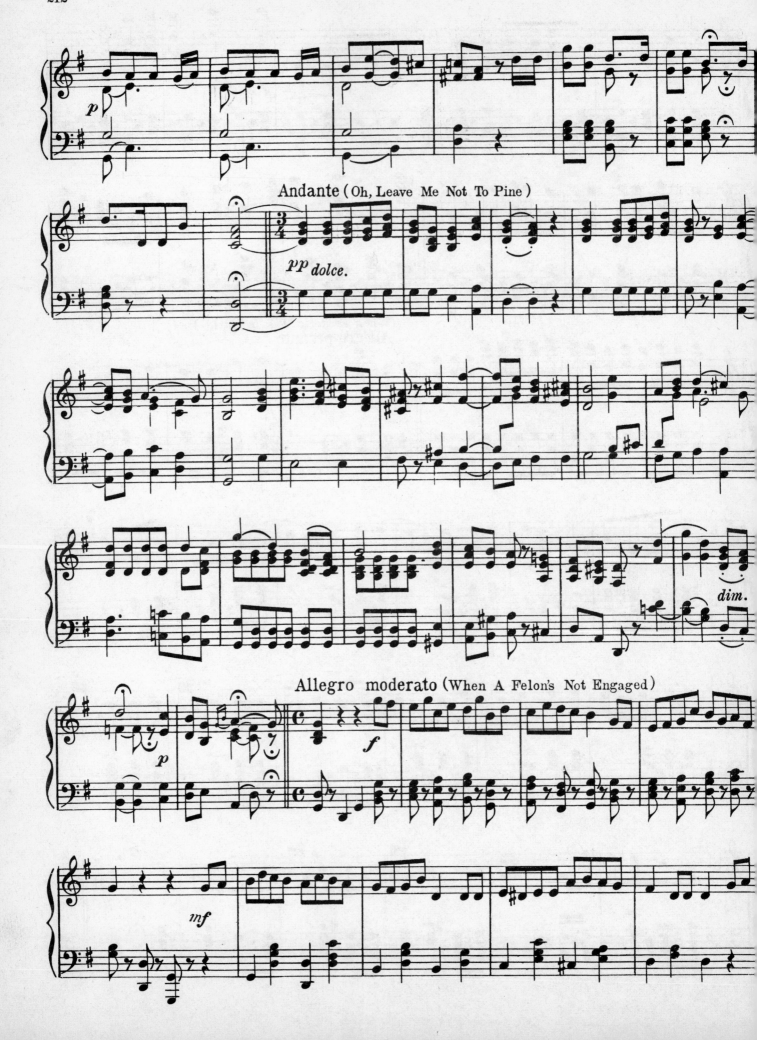

Andante (Oh, Leave Me Not To Pine)

Allegro moderato (When A Felon's Not Engaged)

Allegro vivace

Andante ARIA. (O Is There Not One Maiden)

214

(Poor Wandering One)
Tempo di Valse

Allegro moderato (Tarantara Tarantara)

Maestoso (Burglars' Chorus)

H. M. S. Pinafore
Selected Melodies

Arthur Sullivan

Andante (Sorry her Lot)

cresc.

f

Ped. ※ Ped. ※ Ped. ※

Allegretto (Im called little Buttercup)

p

Ped. ※ Ped. ※ Ped. ※ Ped. simile

Allegretto (I am the Captain of the "Pinafore")

Patience
Selected Melodies

Arthur Sullivan

Allegretto (Prithee, Pretty Maiden)

Allegretto (A Magnet Hung in a Hardware Shop)

Andante moderato (Silver'd is the Raven Hair)

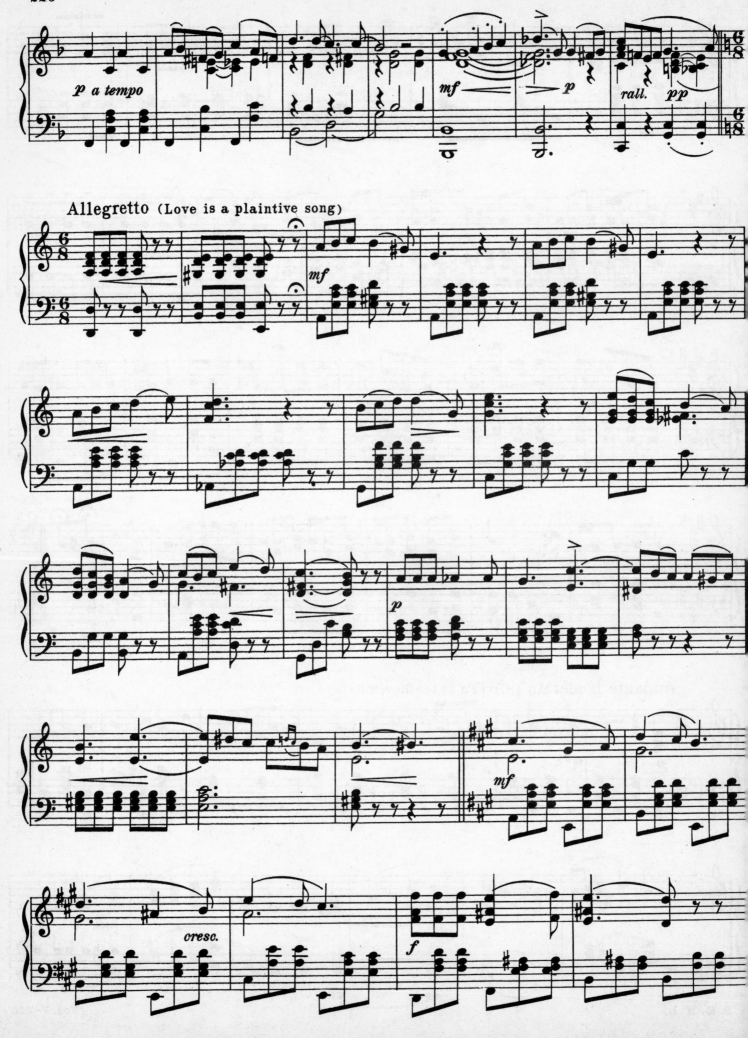

Allegretto (Love is a plaintive song)

Allegretto agitato (Finale)

Ruddigore
Selected Melodies

Arthur Sullivan

Tempo di Valse lente (Waltz)

Allegretto

Tempo di Gavotte

Allegro moderato (Duet)

Allegro (Finale - Act II)

The Mikado
Selected Melodies

Allegro (The Flowers That Bloom in the Spring)

Arthur Sullivan

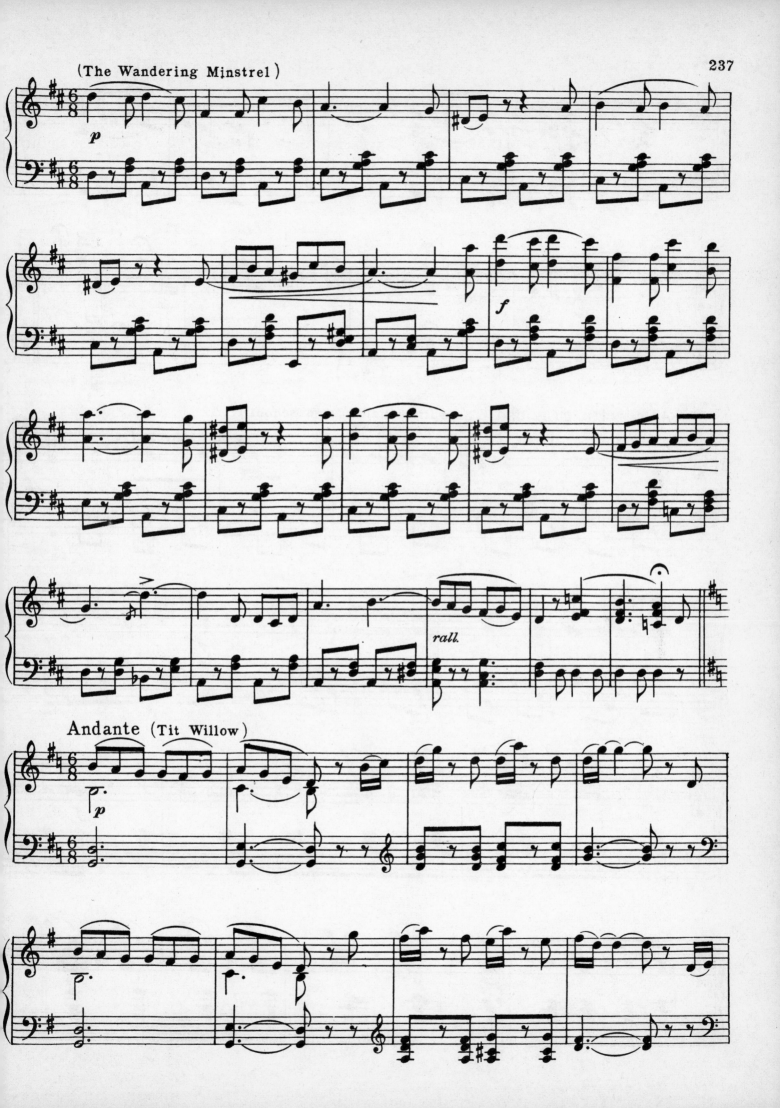

Allegretto grazioso (Three little maids from school)

Allegretto (For he's going to marry Yum-Yum)

Allegro vivace (Here's a how-de-do!)

Più vivo (FINALE)

Iolanthe
Selected Melodies

Arthur Sullivan

Allegro Maestoso (March of the Peers)

cres - - cen - do   ff   p

Andante non troppo (None Shall Part Us)

Tempo di Valse (If You Go In)

Moderato (Sentry's Song)

Allegretto moderato

Andante (Oh Foolish Fay)

Allegro vivo (Finale Act I)

The Gondoliers

Arthur Sullivan

Allegro con brio (Gondolier's Song)

Allegretto grazioso (Good Morning, Ladies)

Allegro con brio (A Regular Royal Queen)

Tempo di Gavotte (I Am a Courtier)

Tempo di Cachucha

Chorus and Dance